AND THAT'S MY FINAL OFFER!

Uncle Duke is lured into a $100,000 gig by a gutless, gouging oil pusher, James "Obscene Profits" Andrews, who contends that from Valdez to Abu Dhabi, the accountants control the world's oil, the barrels are just figures on a computer printout—and the key man is the anonymous, underpaid computer! In Iran today, that man is Hassan Abadan, code-named "Dipstick." So begins another Doonesbury adventure which features such favorites as Joanie Caucus, Rick Redfern, Henry Kissinger (author of "The Whitewash Years"), and David Halberstam, soon-to-be-author of "La Crème de la Crème," who says about Woodward and Bernstein, "Gods. I kiss their Guccis." This is first-rate Doonesbury.

DOONESBURY

The remarkable comic strip called DOONESBURY has provoked more public and media reaction than any cartoon in the last twenty-five years, winning legions of loyal followers, as well as the Pulitzer Prize. The Walden crew and other bizarre denizens appear in nearly four hundred newspapers with a readership of over 23 million.

a Doonesbury book by

G B Trudeau

And That's My Final Offer!

BANTAM BOOKS
Toronto / New York / London / Sydney

AND THAT'S MY FINAL OFFER!

A Bantam Book / published by arrangement with
Holt, Rinehart and Winston

PRINTING HISTORY
Holt, Rinehart and Winston edition published September 1980
Bantam edition / January 1982

The cartoons in this book appeared in newspapers in the United States and
abroad under the auspices of Universal Press Syndicate.

ISBN 0-553-20203-0

Published simultaneously in the United States and Canada

Bantam Books are published by Bantam Books, Inc. Its trade-
mark, consisting of the words "Bantam Books" and the por-
trayal of a rooster, is Registered in U.S. Patent and Trademark
Office and in other countries. Marca Registrada. Bantam
Books, Inc., 666 Fifth Avenue, New York, New York 10103.

PRINTED IN THE UNITED STATES OF AMERICA

10 9 8 7 6 5 4 3 2 1

YOU SEE, DUKE, COMMODITIES ARE A CONCEPTUAL BUSINESS. SURE, THE OIL EXISTS, BUT NO ONE EVER SEES IT. THE BARRELS ARE JUST FIGURES ON A COMPUTER PRINTOUT.

SO WHO REALLY CONTROLS THE FLOW OF OIL? THE ACCOUNTANTS, MY FRIEND! FROM VALDEZ TO ABU DHABI, THE KEY MAN IS THE ANONYMOUS, UNDERPAID, COMPUTER JOCKEY!

IN IRAN TODAY, THAT MAN IS HASSAN ABADAN, CODE-NAMED "DIPSTICK." HIS IS A FAMILIAR STORY. EVEN THOUGH HE'S THE CHIEF ACCOUNTANT AT THE AHVAZ OILFIELDS..

DON'T TELL ME—HIS KIDS NEED BRACES AND HE'S BEHIND ON HIS MORTGAGE.

DUKE, THE DIRECTORS OF UNIVERSAL PETROLEUM JUST DON'T THINK THAT'S FAIR!

GBTrudeau

It's an enormous privilege to meet you, Mr. Redfern, an incredible, extraordinary privilege!

Thank you, Mr. Halberstam. I understand you're working on a sequel to "Powers That Be."

That's right. I'm calling it "La crème de la crème."

The book is about the giants of journalism, the big, very big men, forcing life to exist on their terms, that's how big they are!

Exit, Joanie, stage left.

Where do you want me?

Wherever. Say, isn't that the great smell of Brut?

OKAY, THAT BRINGS US UP TO THE LONG, HOT SUMMER OF '68. THAT'S WHEN YOU WERE SENT TO WASHINGTON TO COVER RESURRECTION CITY, RIGHT?

UM.. YEAH, THAT'S RIGHT..

AND IT WAS THERE THAT YOU BECAME SOMETHING OF A DEITY TO YOUR COLLEAGUES, THEY WERE IN AWE OF YOU, BUT THAT DID NOT LESSEN YOUR DEDICATION, IT INCREASED IT, RIGHT?

I JUST DIDN'T KNOW ANY OTHER WAY, DAVID.

OF COURSE, YOU DIDN'T. *GOD*, YOU LOVED YOUR WORK!

GBTrudeau

DAVID, BEFORE WE GO ON, I GOTTA ASK YOU—DO YOU REALLY BELIEVE IN THIS JOURNALIST-AS-STAR NONSENSE?

GOD, NO! IT'S THE WORST THING THAT CAN HAPPEN TO BOTH JOURNALISM AND THE PUBLIC!

BUT YOUR BOOKS ARE A MONUMENT TO JUST THAT ADULATION!

MAYBE. DEBATABLE. SUBJECT TO DEBATE. BUT I THINK I SEE YOUR POINT..

WHAT YOU'RE SAYING IS THAT THE CELEBRATION OF THE JOURNALIST IS CORRUPTING, THAT WHEN HE BECOMES BIGGER, MUCH BIGGER, THAN HIS STORY, IT DOES NOT HEIGHTEN HIS EFFECTIVENESS, IT DIMINISHES IT, RIGHT?

EXACTLY. TAKE WOODWARD AND BERNSTEIN..

GODS. I KISS THEIR GUCCIS.

GBTrudeau

DAVID, THIS HAS GOT TO STOP. I CAN'T FEEL THE CAFFEINE ANYMORE..

HANG IN THERE, BUDDY. WE STILL HAVE TO TALK ABOUT POWER, HOW IT'S AFFECTED YOU..

POWER? **WHAT** POWER? DAVID, ALL I'VE GOT IS A 30-DAY CONTRACT AT THE "POST," A 5'x5' CUBICLE, AND A MODEST REPUTATION FOR GETTING MY FACTS STRAIGHT!

INFLUENCE IS NOT THE SAME THING AS POWER, DAVID. IN TERMS OF MAKING DECISIONS THAT DIRECTLY AFFECT LIVES, THE LOWLIEST BUREAUCRAT HAS MORE POWER THAN I DO!

I MEAN, I HATE TO BURST YOUR BUBBLE, BUT..

"HE WAS UNGODLY MODEST. HIS MODESTY COULD FILL UP A ROOM.."

I'M SURPRISED TO HEAR YOU QUESTION YOUR OWN POWER, DICK. AFTER ALL, THE PRESS STOPPED A WAR, IT FELLED A PRESIDENT, IT..

OH, DAVID, THAT'S JUST NON-SENSE!

THE PRESS DIDN'T STOP VIETNAM, ALL IT DID WAS REFLECT A GROWING NATIONAL CONSENSUS. WALTER CRONKITE MAY HAVE PACED PUBLIC OPINION, BUT HE NEVER LED IT!

AND SURE, THE PRESS KEPT WATERGATE ALIVE, BUT IT WAS THE COURTS AND NIXON'S OWN TAPES THAT ULTIMATELY FORCED CONGRESS TO MOVE, NOT THE DAMN PRESS!

WE BETTER CALL IT A NIGHT, JOAN, HE'S STARTING TO BABBLE..

RICHARD? IT'S ALL OVER, HONEY. HE'S LEAVING..

G B Trudeau

MR. McMEEL? ANDREWS HERE. I'M AFRAID I HAVE BAD NEWS, SIR. "EAGLE" HAS BOMBED.

DAMN! YOU SURE?

YES, SIR. IF HE TALKS, IT COULD BE EMBARRASSING FOR THE COMPANY! THE WORD IS HE'LL BE TRIED AND EXECUTED IN THE MORNING.

MY GOD.. THAT'S TERRIBLE..

YES, SIR. HE WAS A GOOD FRIEND.

YOU GOT SOMEONE ELSE LINED UP?

YEAH, BUT I THINK WE OUGHTA WAIT A DECENT INTERVAL. AT LEAST UNTIL THE STOCK MARKET CLOSES.

GBTrudeau

GOOD EVENING. TODAY FORMER UNITED STATES AMBASSADOR DUKE WAS CAPTURED WHILE PARACHUTING INTO THE AHVAZ OIL FIELDS IN IRAN. ROLAND HEDLEY HAS DETAILS.

THE REVOLUTIONARY GOVERNMENT OF THE AYATOLLAH KHOMEINI ANNOUNCED TONIGHT THAT THE ONETIME WASHINGTON REDSKINS FIELD GENERAL WOULD BE TRIED AND CONVICTED OF HIGH CRIMES AGAINST GOD.

ALTHOUGH DUE PROCESS AS PRACTICED IN THE WEST IS VIRTUALLY UNKNOWN HERE, ABC NEWS HAS LEARNED THAT AMBASSADOR DUKE WAS PERMITTED THE CUSTOMARY PHONE CALL..

HEY, MAN, THOSE ARE THE BREAKS.

DAMMIT, BRENNER! I NEED THOSE KRUGERRANDS!

G B Trudeau

THIS IS ROLAND HEDLEY. IT'S A BLEAK, DARK MORNING HERE IN TEHERAN AS THE ESPIONAGE TRIAL OF FORMER AMBASSADOR DUKE GETS UNDER WAY!

IN THE NEW IRAN, THE ISLAMIC KANGAROO COURTS ARE CUSTOMARILY GAVELED TO ORDER AT AN UNGODLY 4:00 A.M.! TODAY SHOULD BE NO EXCEPTION.

TENSION HAS BEEN MOUNTING HERE ALL WEEK AS..

THE WHOLE WORLD IS *WATCHING!* THE WHOLE WORLD IS *WATCHING!*

AH, HERE COMES THE DEFENDANT NOW!

THE WHOLE.. >THUD!< UNH!

GBTrudeau

MR. DUKE WAS THEN DRAGGED SCREAMING AND KICKING TO THE GRAVEL ROOFTOP OF THE COURTHOUSE, A POPULAR SPOT IN RECENT MONTHS FOR DISCIPLINING FORMER SAVAK AGENTS.

AS YET, HOWEVER, THERE HAS BEEN NO OFFICIAL INDICATION THAT THE SENTENCE HAS BEEN CARRIED OUT. CERTAINLY THIS REPORTER HAS HEARD NO SHOTS, AND HE HAS KEPT HIS EARS PRICKED.

MOREOVER, THERE ARE NOW REPORTS THAT SENSITIVE NEGOTIATIONS MAY BE UNDER WAY IN A LAST-DITCH ATTEMPT TO SAVE THE FORMER AMBASSADOR'S LIFE.

$500,000! IN GOLD!

$250,000! AND THAT'S MY FINAL OFFER!

CHING? HI, IT'S YOUR NEW ROOM-MATE, JOAN CAUCUS..

LISTEN, I'LL BE MOVING IN TOMORROW MORNING. I'M OVER AT MY MOM'S PLACE NOW. WOULD YOU LIKE TO COME OVER FOR DINNER?

WHAT?.. WHY NOT?

I'M TOO UPSET. MY BOYFRIEND'S BEEN SENTENCED TO DEATH.

GBTrudeau

GOOD EVENING. TODAY "OPERATION MANHOOD" WENT INTO HIGH GEAR AS SENATORS CHURCH, JACKSON AND BAKER FORMALLY OPENED THEIR SPECIAL LINKAGE HEARINGS.

WAVING A PARCHMENT COPY OF THE MONROE DOCTRINE ABOVE HIS HEAD, JACKSON DEMANDED THAT THE PRESIDENT FACE DOWN THE SOVIETS "EYEBALL TO EYEBALL, LIKE A REAL MAN."

IN ANOTHER DEVELOPMENT, THE SENATORS ALSO PLEDGED TO INVESTIGATE NEW EVIDENCE LINKING RUSSIAN SABOTEURS WITH THE SINKING OF THE "MAINE."

FROM THE CHEAP SEATS ON CAPITOL HILL, THIS IS ROLAND HEDLEY, JR.

G B Trudeau

GENERAL, LET'S GET RIGHT DOWN TO BRASS TACKS! IS THE SOVIET UNION TURNING CUBA INTO A FORTRESS-STATE?

WELL, THE EVIDENCE CERTAINLY SUGGESTS SO, SENATOR JACKSON.

FOR INSTANCE, A RECENT SR-71 FLIGHT BROUGHT BACK SOME AERIAL PHOTOGRAPHS OF A CUBAN MILITARY SUPPLY DEPOT. ONE OF THE PHOTOGRAPHS REVEALED A SOVIET COMMISSARY OFFICER EXAMINING A REQUISITION FORM..

WHEN TRANSLATED FROM THE ORIGINAL SPANISH, THE FORM WAS FOUND TO CONTAIN A REQUEST FOR NEARLY 1,500 CZECH STAPLE GUNS.

STAPLE GUNS? WITH AN OFFENSIVE CAPABILITY?

LET'S JUST SAY THE TECHNOLOGY IS AVAILABLE.

GBTrudeau

SENATOR CHURCH, IF I MAY JUST MAKE ONE LAST COMMENT..

OF COURSE, GENERAL.

SENATOR, I THINK IT'S FAIR TO SAY THAT IF IT HAD NOT BEEN FOR THE VIGILANCE OF THE U.S. SENATE, THIS MAJOR CRISIS IN CUBA MIGHT HAVE DEGENERATED INTO A MINOR DIPLOMATIC SQUABBLE EASILY HANDLED BY THE STATE DEPARTMENT.

BY REFUSING TO FAN THE FLAMES OF MODERATION, A CALM, NEGOTIATED SOLUTION HAS BEEN NARROWLY AVERTED. THANKS TO YOU AND "OPERATION MANHOOD," THE AMERICAN PEOPLE HAVE BEEN GIVEN ANOTHER CHANCE TO SHOW THAT THEY'RE STILL NUMBER ONE!

THANK YOU, GENERAL, I APPRECIATE THAT.

THANK YOU, SENATOR. AND GOOD LUCK WITH YOUR RE-ELECTION.

GBTrudeau

GOOD EVENING. TODAY "TIME" MAGAZINE PUBLISHED PART II OF THE MOST TRUMPETED MEMOIRS IN HISTORY— "HENRY KISSINGER, THE WHITEWASH YEARS."

AFTER A SUMMER OF FAWNING KISSINGER STORIES, "TIME" HAS FINALLY ARRIVED AT THE MAIN EVENT— AN ORGY OF EXCERPTS FROM A BOOK "TIME" ITSELF WILL PUBLISH..

IS THIS HOW THE RULING CLASS PROMOTES ITS OWN? I'M ROLAND HEDLEY. STAY WITH US FOR A LOOK AT WHAT HAPPENS WHEN A NEWS-WEEKLY DECIDES TO.. HYPE HENRY!

"HYPE HENRY: MEMOIRS ON THE MAKE," BROUGHT TO YOU BY THE CHASE MANHATTAN BANK..

HENRY KISSINGER'S "THE WHITE-WASH YEARS" IS NO ORDINARY BOOK. NOR IS "TIME" PROMOTING IT LIKE ONE. BILL WOOTEN, "TIME" MARKETING DIRECTOR, EXPLAINS.

WELL, WE STARTED SLOW, OF COURSE. WE RAN THE USUAL SEMIANNUAL KISSINGER PROFILES, REPORTS ON THE WORK-IN-PROGRESS, A FEW MENTIONS IN OUR "PEOPLE" SECTION..

THEN THIS SUMMER, WE POURED IT ON! AN EXCLUSIVE INTERVIEW, A FOUR-PAGE COLOR SPREAD ON HIS SALT LECTURE, TWO PAGES ON HIS NATO SPEECH! I MEAN, WE PUFFED OL' HENRY FROM HERE TO SUNDAY!

DO ANY NEWS STORIES?

UM.. WE MIGHT HAVE. THAT'S NOT MY DE-PARTMENT.

GBTrudeau

POLITICAL MEMOIRS ARE NOTORIOUSLY SELF-SERVING, AND "WHITEWASH YEARS" IS NO EXCEPTION. SO IS THE BOOK OF ANY HISTORICAL VALUE? WE ASKED HISTORIAN LEO PARTCH.

WELL, IT'S HARD TO TELL, REALLY, BECAUSE THERE'S SO LITTLE IN THE LITERATURE TO WEIGH IT AGAINST.

SO FAR THE ONLY BOOKS ON KISSINGER HAVE BEEN WRITTEN BY OBSEQUIOUS T.V. CORRESPONDENTS WHO STILL TREMBLE AT THE HONOR OF ADDRESSING HIM BY HIS FIRST NAME.

FOR THE RECORD, THIS REPORTER HAS NEVER ENJOYED "HENRY" PRIVILEGES. BACK AFTER THIS.

GB Trudeau

AND SO THE BIG QUESTION AT TIME, INC., IS THIS: WILL SURVIVORS OF THE NIXON-KISSINGER ERA ACTUALLY BE TEMPTED TO PAY MONEY TO RELIVE IT?

700,000 WORDS. 1,521 PAGES. THE 30-MONTH OUTPUT OF KISSINGER'S HANDPICKED MEMOIR STAFF. BY ALMOST ANY STANDARD, "WHITEWASH YEARS" IS A VERY BIG BOOK!

GRANTED, HENRY KISSINGER HAD MUCH TO ANSWER FOR, BUT NEED SO MANY TREES HAVE DIED FOR THE CAUSE? MOST KISSINGER SCHOLARS THINK NOT.

HELL, IT ONLY TOOK ALBERT SPEER 520 PAGES..

THANK YOU, MR. WEINBURGER! ANY OTHER COMMENTS?

I THINK THE WORST THING IS BEING IN LIMBO, J.J., STILL NOT KNOWING WHAT REALLY HAPPENED TO DUKE..

EVEN IF HE MANAGED TO CHEAT DEATH AT THE LAST MINUTE, WHO KNOWS WHEN I'LL SEE HIM NEXT? IT COULD BE MONTHS, YEARS!

I'M PRETTY SURE HE'D WANT ME TO DATE AROUND, THOUGH.

WOW.. HE SOUNDS LIKE QUITE A GUY.

MR. PRESIDENT? THE NEW CAUCUS FUTURES HAVE ARRIVED, SIR.

THE NEW WHAT, HAM?

THE LATEST PRESS PREDICTIONS ON HOW WELL WE'RE SUPPOSED TO DO IN UPCOMING CAUCUSES, SIR..

THE NEXT ONE SEEMS TO BE THE MAHASKA COUNTY CAUCUS IN IOWA. IT'S A NONBINDING PREFERENTIAL POLL TO ELECT HONORARY, NONVOTING DELEGATES TO THE STRAW POLL AT THE STATE FAIR.

STATE FAIR?

IF WE GET LESS THAN 60%, IT'S A MORAL VICTORY FOR KENNEDY.

WHAT'S IT SAY, ZONK?

"REGRET TO INFORM YOU YOUR UNCLE DUKE HAS BEEN DECLARED LEGALLY DEAD."

"READING OF WILL SCHEDULED FOR MONDAY. PLEASE COME SOONEST TO HELP ORGANIZE PERSONAL EFFECTS. CONDOLENCES. T. BANNON, ATTORNEY-AT-LAW."

GEE.. WHO DO YOU SUPPOSE MOVED TO HAVE HIM DECLARED LEGALLY DEAD?

I'M NOT SURE, BUT I'VE GOT A PRETTY GOOD IDEA!

YOU WANT THE STEREO PACKED TOO, BUDDY?

NO, NO, JUST PUT IT IN THE BACK OF MY VAN.

"JAN. 16, 1975, PAGO PAGO. ARRIVED TODAY TO SERVE IN MY CAPACITY AS NEWLY APPOINTED GOVERNOR OF AMERICAN SAMOA."

"RECEPTION WAS MAGNIFICENT. GREETED BY 21-GUN SALUTE, AND MY NEW AIDE-DE-CAMP, MACARTHUR, PRESENTED ME WITH A SILVER THERMOS OF DAIQUIRIS."

"HAVE TAKEN INSTANT LIKING TO SAMOAN PEOPLE, ESPECIALLY STAFF AT GOVERNOR'S MANSION. THEY ARE GENTLE, WARM, AND POSSESSED OF AN ALMOST CHILDLIKE INNOCENCE."

"JAN. 17. HONEYMOON OVER. FOUND SEED IN ORANGE JUICE. HAD COOK FLOGGED."

GBTrudeau

"FEB. 16, 1976. PEKING. WELCOME BANQUET IS BIG SUCCESS."

"THE TOASTS SEEMED ENDLESS, SURELY NO AMERICAN ENVOY HAS EVER BEEN RECEIVED WITH SUCH OPEN AFFECTION."

"MY DISTINGUISHED RECORD OF WORKING WITH MINORITIES HAD OBVIOUSLY PRECEDED ME. ALSO, FACT THAT I GAVE TOAST IN JAPANESE SEEMS TO HAVE MADE QUITE AN IMPRESSION."

"FEB. 17. SENT MAO NEW RESPIRATORY TENT WITH MY COMPLIMENTS."

GBTrudeau

YOU HEARD ME, PAL. PUT IT ALL IN ESCROW. NO ONE TOUCHES DUKE'S ESTATE UNTIL I SAY SO!

BUT, MR. HARRIS, WE'VE WORKED OUT A WHOLE INVESTMENT PROGRAM FOR YOU..

I'LL JUST BET YOU HAVE! WELL, YOU CAN FORGET IT! NOW, I HAVE A PLANE TO CATCH.

BE REASONABLE, MAN. WE COULD PUT YOUR MONEY TO WORK!

NO! AND THAT'S FINAL!

YOU'LL HAVE HIM DECLARED INSANE, OF COURSE.

CAN'T. THE JUDGE I USE IS ON VACATION.

GBTrudeau

GOOD EVENING. TODAY THE SMALL TOWN OF ROSE-WATER, INDIANA, WAS HIT SUDDENLY BY A THREE-NETWORK MEDIA EVENT. IT WAS THE WORST ME-DIA EVENT IN RECENT MEMORY.

THERE HAD BEEN NO WARN-ING. WHEN THE TINY LOCAL REPUBLICAN CAUCUS CON-VENED LAST NIGHT FOR ITS PRESIDENTIAL STRAW POLL, ONLY LIGHT COV-ERAGE HAD BEEN FORE-CASTED..

BUT BEFORE IT WAS OVER, THE UNSUSPECTING TOWN WOULD BE BUFFETED BY WAVE AFTER WAVE OF REPORTERS, ITS CITIZENS INTERVIEWED AGAIN AND AGAIN, LEAVING THEM DAZED AND FAMOUS. ROLAND HEDLEY HAS DETAILS.

PEOPLE WERE JUST SITTING DOWN TO DIN-NER WHEN WALTER CRONKITE'S LIMOUSINE GLIDED UP TO RAY'S TACKLE SHOP..

©B Trudeau

THIS IS ROLAND HEDLEY. IT WAS SHORTLY AFTER DUSK WHEN THE MEDIA EVENT FIRST SWEPT THROUGH THE SMALL HOOSIER HAMLET OF ROSEWATER...

MEMBERS OF THE ROSEWATER G.O.P. CAUCUS HAD JUST CAST THE FIRST BALLOT IN A PRESIDENTIAL STRAW POLL. CAUCUS MEMBER AL FENDER EXPLAINS WHAT HAPPENED NEXT.

IT WAS AWFUL. THE HOT LIGHTS, THE CAMERAS. SOME OF US TRIED TO STAY OFF THE RECORD, BUT IT WAS HOPELESS. WE WERE FORCED TO STAND BY HELPLESSLY AS OUR REMARKS WERE BLOWN ALL OUT OF PROPORTION!

AND THE POLL RESULTS?

STRIPPED OF THEIR CONTEXT! RIGHT THERE IN FRONT OF OUR FAMILIES!

A MEDIA EVENT. UNTIL LAST NIGHT, FOR THE PEOPLE OF ROSEWATER IT HAD ONLY BEEN AN EXPRESSION. VICTIMS RAY AND ELLEN McNEIL RECALL THEIR NIGHTMARE.

I GUESS IT STARTED RIGHT AFTER THE CAUCUS VOTE. THE FAMILY HAD PICKED ME UP AT THE VFW HALL, AND WE WALKED THE FEW BLOCKS HOME..

AS WE GOT TO THE FRONT YARD, I SEE THIS FELLER IN A SAFARI-TYPE JACKET RUNNING AT US. HE WAS YELLING AND WAVING AND KEPT TRIPPING OVER THIS LONG, PURPLE SCARF. IT WAS GERALDO RIVERA.

"GET THE KIDS INSIDE," I SHOUTED TO ELLEN..

WE WERE SCARED. WE'D SEEN WHAT HE'D DONE TO ELVIS'S DOCTOR.

GBTrudeau

FOR THE CITIZENS OF ROSEWATER, THE MEDIA EVENT IS OVER. BUT THE SCARS LINGER ON. CAUCUS MEMBER SHELLY SIMMS SHARES HER TRAUMA AND SHAME.

WELL, I WAS JUST LEAVING THE VFW HALL WHEN I FIRST SAW THEM. I TRIED TO FLEE, BUT THERE WERE TOO MANY OF THEM. A BIG ONE, WITH A MICROPHONE, CORNERED ME..

I TRIED TO RESIST, I TRIED TO TELL HIM IT WAS JUST A STRAW POLL, THAT IT DIDN'T MEAN ANYTHING, BUT HE..HE..

HE WHAT, MS. SIMMS?

HE INTER-VIEWED ME! REPEAT-EDLY!

WHO, MS. SIMMS? WHO DID THIS TO YOU? WAS IT ROGER MUDD?

©BTrudeau

NOW THAT THE MEDIA CIRCUS HAS LEFT TOWN, THE VICTIMS OF THIS SENSE-LESS, MINDLESS COVERAGE MUST TRY TO PICK UP THE PIECES. HOMEMAKER DOTTY HOLMES TALKS OF HER DESPAIR.

IT'S HARDEST ON MY THREE KIDS. THEY'RE HEARTBROKEN. THEY KEEP ASKING ME, "MOMMY, WHEN ARE THE T.V. PEOPLE COMING BACK?"

I DON'T KNOW WHAT WE'LL DO. ABC NEWS PROMISED US THERE'D BE A FOLLOW-UP STORY, BUT WE DON'T HAVE MUCH HOPE THAT ANYTHING WILL COME OF IT..

THIS IS THE FOLLOW-UP STORY, MRS. HOLMES.

OH. WELL, IT'S JUST NOT THE SAME.

GB Trudeau

WILL ROSEWATER EVER RECOVER? WELL, STUDIES OF THE CITIZENS OF PLAINS, GEORGIA, HAVE SHOWN THAT VICTIMS OF A MEDIA EVENT OFTEN EXPERIENCE A SEVERE LETDOWN ONCE THE KLEIG LIGHTS HAVE BEEN TURNED OFF..

WHETHER THE SAME WILL HAPPEN TO THE DENIZENS OF ROSEWATER REMAINS TO BE SEEN. ONE THING, HOWEVER, IS CLEAR: LIFE, AS IS ITS WONT, GOES ON. FRANK?

THANK YOU, ROLAND. AS PART OF OUR NONSTOP PRESIDENTIAL CAMPAIGN COVERAGE, TONIGHT AT 8:00 P.M. ABC WILL PRESENT A SPECIAL REPORT ON THE REPORTERS WHO ATTENDED THE ROSEWATER MEDIA EVENT.

COMING UP: TEDDY SAYS HE'S NEVER PANICKED DURING A MALAISE.

GBTrudeau

A SEVENTIES REVIVAL PARTY! I LIKE IT!

WELL, I THOUGHT WE SHOULD GET IT OVER WITH. BESIDES, IT'S RIFE WITH POS- SIBILITIES!

IT SURE IS! I THINK I'LL COME AS A MOONIE.

YOU'LL NEVER GET IN.

I WON'T?

NOPE. WE'RE HIRING BOUNCERS. GUESTS WHO AREN'T FAMOUS WILL HAVE TO WAIT OUTSIDE IN THE COLD FOR 15 MINUTES.

I GUESS YOU HAVE TO DRAW THE LINE SOMEWHERE.

RIGHT. BESIDES, ANYONE WHO COULDN'T GET ON A TALK SHOW DURING THE '70s WASN'T TRYING.

GBTrudeau

HI, RICK. LOOK, I HAVE TO MEET ZEKE AT THE AIRPORT, SO I CAN'T STAY FOR VERY LONG..

IT'S PROBABLY JUST AS WELL. MOM'S BEEN ON MY CASE A LOT LATELY, WHICH I'M NOT SURE SHE'S ENTITLED TO. YOU GUYS HAVEN'T BEEN FIGHTING, HAVE YOU?

LISTEN, WHEN I BRING ZEKE BY AFTER DINNER, TRY NOT TO BE TOO JUDGMENTAL, OKAY? HE'S A LIBRA AND VERY SENSITIVE.

HI, JOAN. WON'T YOU COME IN?

OH, MOM! YOU'RE NOT SERVING MEAT!

GBTrudeau

LATE TERM PAPERS.
MISSED EXAMS. IRON-
ICALLY, OBSERVERS NOW
BELIEVE THAT MOUNTING
ACADEMIC PRESSURE MAY
BE THE KEY TO THE FINAL
RELEASE OF THE HOSTAGES.

ALL OF THIS IS FEVERISHLY
DENIED BY THE STUDENTS
THEMSELVES. TEHRAN SOPH-
OMORE HASH AFSHAR IS HERE
IN OUR EMBASSY STUDIO TO
PRESENT THE STUDENTS'
POINT OF VIEW.

HOWEVER, NBC NEWS OFFERS A
WORD OF CAUTION. VIEWERS SHOULD
BE ON THE LOOKOUT FOR ANY AT-
TEMPT BY THE STUDENT TO MANIPU-
LATE THE MEDIUM OF TELEVISION
TO CREATE SYMPATHY FOR
HIS POSITION.

NOW THEN,
MR. AFSHAR..

DEATH TO
CARTER.

©B Trudeau